MUMMY GOES TO HOSPITAL

Written by Lynsey and Theo Gregory.
Illustrated by Anne Darwin.
Published by LMD Publications.

Hello!
My name
is **Theo**
and I am
3 years
old.

This is my little sister, Tillie.

We are as happy as can be!

One day my mummy was tired
and she could not play.

So she went to see the doctor.

The doctor told her that she had to go to the hospital for a while.

We packed
Mummy's bag
with clothes...

and lots of happy
things from home.

Mummy had a room at hospital but we could still see her on the screen at home.

I read stories and showed her my toys.

Tillie laughed and smiled.

The doctor told us that Mummy was having super-hero medicine that blasted away the germs and the 'things' that were making her poorly.

Some things stayed the same...

On Monday I still went to Nan's house

On Tuesday I still went to Nursery

On Wednesday I still went to Nursery again.

On Thursday I still went to Tina the childminder.

On Friday I still went to trampoline and singing class

Some things changed.

Nanna lived
at our house.

Daddy looked
after us.
But sometimes
he stayed with
Mummy at the
hospital.

Mummy changed a little.

She cut her hair.

Then her hair came out.

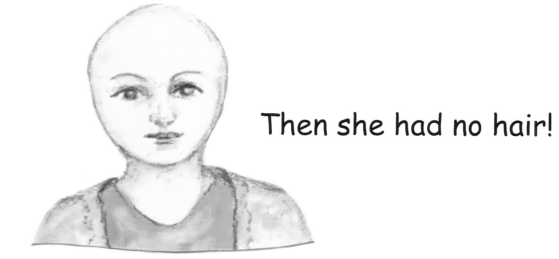

Then she had no hair!

Then she had magic hair!

Magic hair

Despite the changes, she was still
Mummy.

When Mummy was feeling better, she came home.

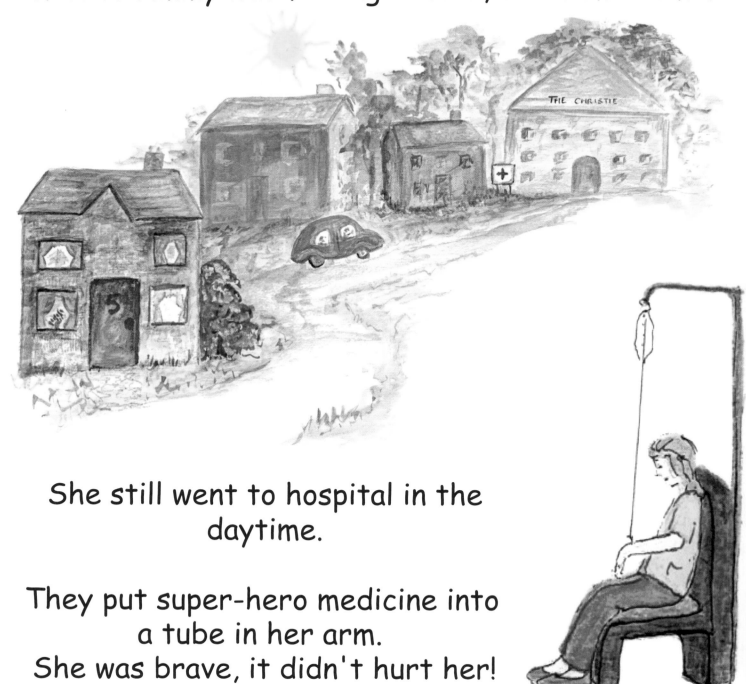

She still went to hospital in the daytime.

They put super-hero medicine into a tube in her arm.
She was brave, it didn't hurt her!

Some days Mummy was tired, we needed to let her rest.

To help keep the germs away, we wore magical masks.

We decorated our masks to make them fun.

Our special teddy bears!

This is my teddy.

This is Tillie's teddy.

Mummy gave us special teddy bears
with her voice in them.
We cuddled our bears when we needed a Mummy hug!

Some of our days are happy.

Some of our days are sad.

But we know that we always stick together as a family.
We love each other very much!